USBORNE KEY SKILLS

Wipe-clean
Dividing

Illustrated by Marta Cabrol

Written by Holly Bathie
Designed by Claire Ever

Lem

Ant

$$10 \div 2 = 5$$

players   teams   players in each team

Froggy

Crock

There are answers, and secret notes for grown-ups at the back of the book.

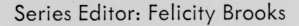

Series Editor: Felicity Brooks

Sorting and sharing

Lem has 12 pieces of fruit to sell at the jungle market.

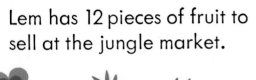

Lem

Help Lem sort the fruit into baskets to sell.

Draw the fruit in the correct basket below. Cross off each piece of fruit on the next page as you draw it.

melons   bananas   oranges

Now trace the numbers and fill in the box to show what you have done.

 sorted into =

pieces of fruit   baskets   pieces of fruit
                                          in each basket

There is an equal number of fruit in each basket.

Wipe the market stall clean.

LEM'S FRESH FRUIT

Lem has decided to share out the fruit into bags instead. She wants one of each kind of fruit in each bag.

Draw a ring around 3 different pieces of fruit to fill a bag. Keep drawing rings around groups of 3 until all the fruit is shared out.

FRUIT

Now trace the numbers and write in the box how many bags Lem will need.

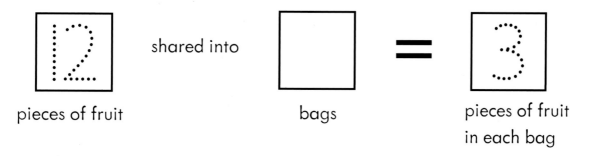

12

pieces of fruit

shared into

bags

=

3

pieces of fruit in each bag

Squawk!

When you are sorting and sharing out an amount, instead of writing this in words, you can use the 'dividing' sign. Beaky is pointing to it.

Dividing by 2 (making 2 equal groups)

Baz, Lem, Cheeky, Froggy and Ant are each out with a friend.
They have found tasty things to share equally for their lunch.

Count how many treats each pair has found.
Now draw rings to divide the treats into two
equal groups and complete the calculations.

$$4 \div 2 = \boxed{} \text{ each}$$

$$\boxed{} \div 2 = \boxed{} \text{ each}$$

Cheeky

Cheeky's friend

$\boxed{} \div \boxed{2} = \boxed{}$ each

Froggy

Froggy's friend

$\boxed{} \div \boxed{2} = \boxed{}$ each

Ant

Ant's friend

$\boxed{} \div \boxed{2} = \boxed{}$ each

Dividing by 5 (making 5 equal groups)

Crock has picked 15 pretty flowers to put on his café tables. Help him to divide the flowers equally between 5 vases.

Crock

Draw a flower in each vase. Draw another flower in each vase. Keep drawing flowers one by one until you have drawn 15 flowers.

There should be an equal number of flowers in each vase.

Complete the calculation to show how many flowers are in each vase.

15 ÷ 5 = ☐ in each vase

Wipe the vases clean.

The other animals are going to help decorate the café each day. Tig will pick 10 flowers to put in the vases. Draw flowers one by one in the vases in the same way, until you have drawn 10 flowers.

Complete the calculation below to show how many flowers are in each vase.

$\boxed{} \div \boxed{5} = \boxed{}$ in each vase

Wipe the vases clean.

I am going to pick 20 flowers for the café.

Sort each animal's flowers into the vases in the same way. Wipe the vases clean each time.

$\boxed{} \div \boxed{5} = \boxed{}$ in each vase

I am going to pick 25 flowers for the café.

$\boxed{} \div \boxed{5} = \boxed{}$ in each vase

I am going to pick 30 flowers for the café.

$\boxed{} \div \boxed{5} = \boxed{}$ in each vase

Dividing by 10 (making 10 equal groups)

The 10 animals are going on a long hike. The jungle store has delivered all the things they need. Help them to divide everything equally between them.

First, count how many maps there are and write the number in the blue box. Now draw lines to match each map with a backpack.

Finish the calculation to show how many maps each animal will get.

$$\boxed{} \div \boxed{10} = \boxed{} \quad \text{each}$$

Wipe away your lines.

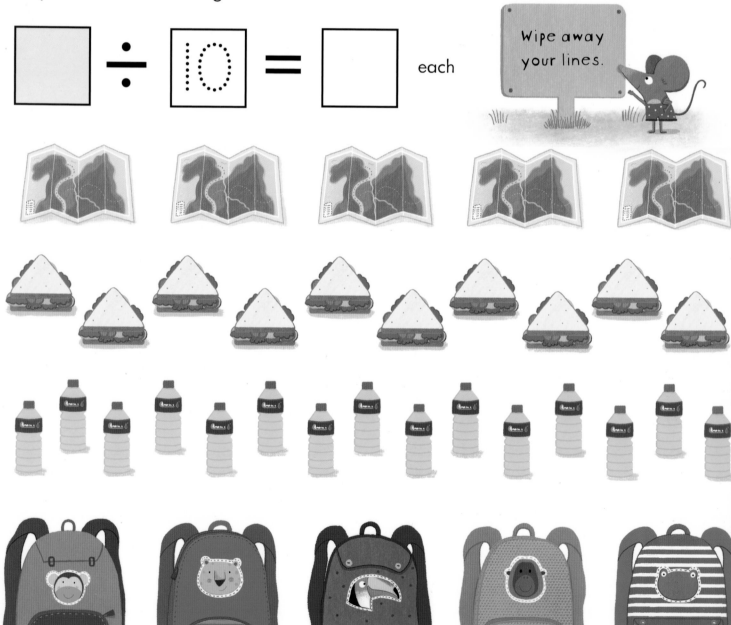

Cheeky   Lep   Beaky   Tan-tan   Froggy

Now count the sandwiches. Draw lines to match a sandwich with each backpack. Keep going until all the sandwiches have been shared out equally.

Complete the calculation to show how many sandwiches each animal will get.

 ÷ = each

Do the same for the water bottles, then complete the calculation.

 ÷ = each

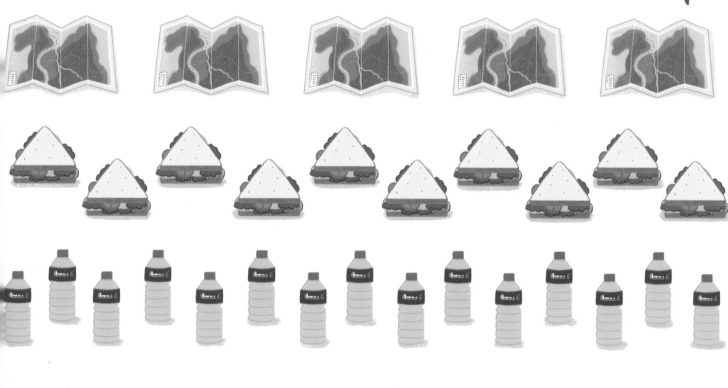

 Tig    Ant    Lem    Baz    Crock

Equal groups

12 monkeys are playing in the trees. An equal number of them are wearing each colour. Draw a big ring around those who are wearing the same colour to make a group. Keep going until all the monkeys are divided into colour groups.

Cheeky

Count how many colour groups there are and then finish the calculation to show what you have done.

 ÷ [ ] = [ ]

monkeys   colours   in each group

Wipe the picture clean.

There are an equal number of monkeys wearing the same type of clothes (such as dresses, shorts, dungarees or T-shirts).

Draw around all the monkeys wearing the same type of clothes to divide them into groups.

Count how many clothes groups there are and then finish the calculation below to show what you have done.

12 ÷ ☐ = ☐

monkeys   types of clothes   in each group

Multiplying and dividing

Froggy and Crock are multiplying to find out how many berries they have. Fill in the boxes to answer their questions.

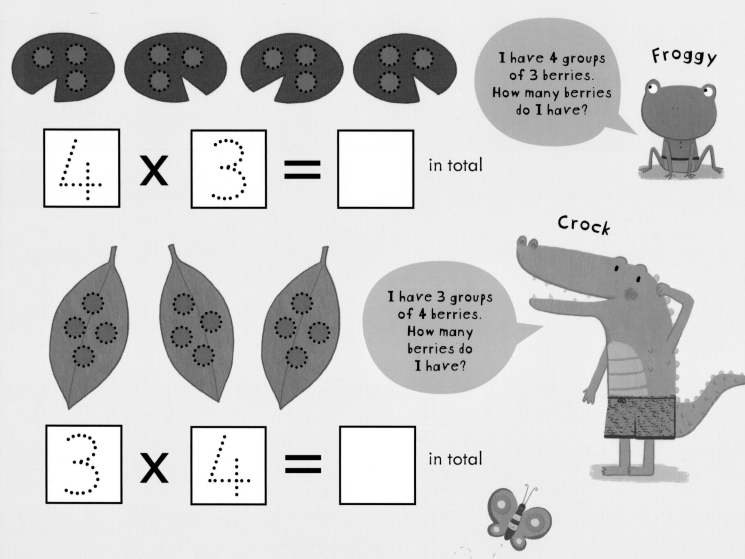

I have 4 groups of 3 berries. How many berries do I have?

Froggy

4 x 3 = ☐ in total

Crock

I have 3 groups of 4 berries. How many berries do I have?

3 x 4 = ☐ in total

Multiplying and dividing are both about equal groups.

Adding groups of the same number (multiplying) tells you how many in total.

Sharing a total amount out into equal groups (dividing) tells you how many in each group.

Squawk!

The friends have gathered up their berries and now divided them into equal groups, to see how many berries will be in each group. Fill in the boxes to answer their questions.

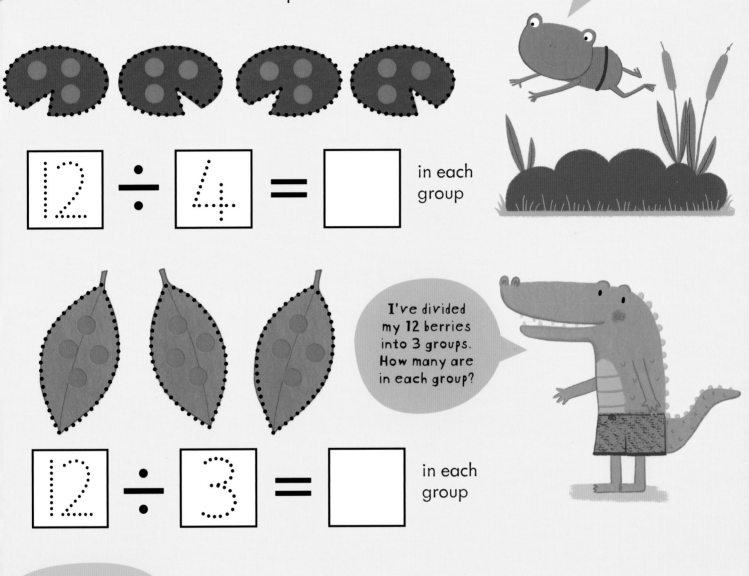

I've divided my 12 berries into 4 groups. How many are in each group?

$$12 \div 4 = \boxed{}$$ in each group

I've divided my 12 berries into 3 groups. How many are in each group?

$$12 \div 3 = \boxed{}$$ in each group

Their berries look the same on each page!

Squawk!

Be careful! You can multiply together equal groups in any order and the answer won't change. However, with dividing, the number of equal groups you divide into will always change the answer, so read dividing questions carefully.

This many each

Lep and Froggy have 12 lemons which they want to sell in bags of 2.

How many customers could we serve before we run out of lemons?

Lep

Froggy

LEP'S LOVELY LEMONS

The animals know how many lemons they have, and how many they want in each group, but they don't know how many equal groups that would make. This is what their dividing calculation looks like:

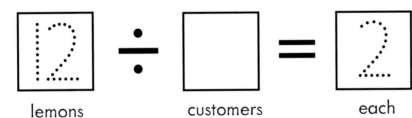

lemons   customers   each

Sometimes it's useful to know lots of multiplying calculations (or times tables) because you can turn a dividing question into a multiplying one, to help you.

Squawk!

I'll count in 2s until I get to 12.

2, 4, 6, 8, 10, 12...

I counted 2 six times. 6 lots of 2 is 12.

$$6 \times 2 = 12$$

So if we divide 12 lemons so that everyone has 2 each, we can serve 6 customers.

Now complete Lep and Froggy's dividing calculation on the opposite page.

Cheeky and Beaky have picked 9 coconuts.
They want to sell them in bags of 3.

How many customers could we serve before we run out of coconuts?

This is Cheeky and Beaky's calculation:

$$9 \div \boxed{} = 3$$

coconuts   customers   each

You could count in 3s to complete their dividing question for them.
Complete the blank multiplying calculation below to help you, if you like.

$$\boxed{} \times 3 = 9$$

2 each (making equal groups of 2)

These things in the jungle shop should be divided up into pairs, so that every customer will get 2 of each thing. Help Ant to work out how many pairs he will have.

Count the items, then draw a ring around each matching pair to make groups of 2 and complete the calculations.

Ant

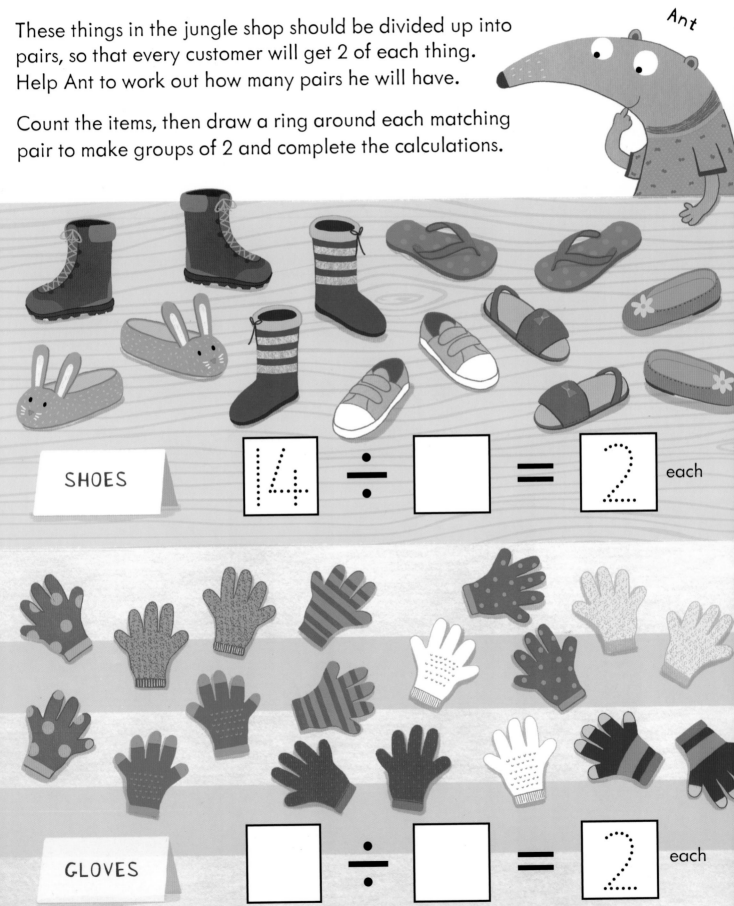

SHOES

14 ÷ ☐ = 2 each

GLOVES

☐ ÷ ☐ = 2 each

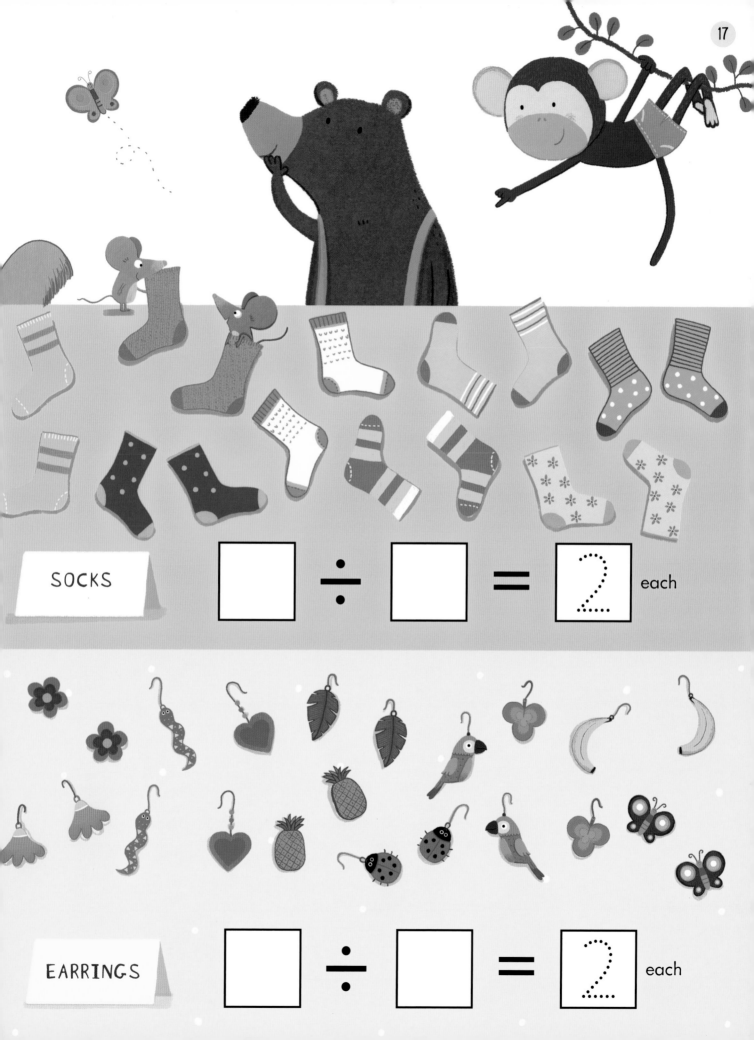

SOCKS

☐ ÷ ☐ = 2 each

EARRINGS

☐ ÷ ☐ = 2 each

5 each (making equal groups of 5)

The café is popular today. Buses full of animals are arriving for Crock's tasty treats. Each table has seats for 5 animals.

Complete the calculation to show how many tables Crock will need for the first 10 customers who are waiting.

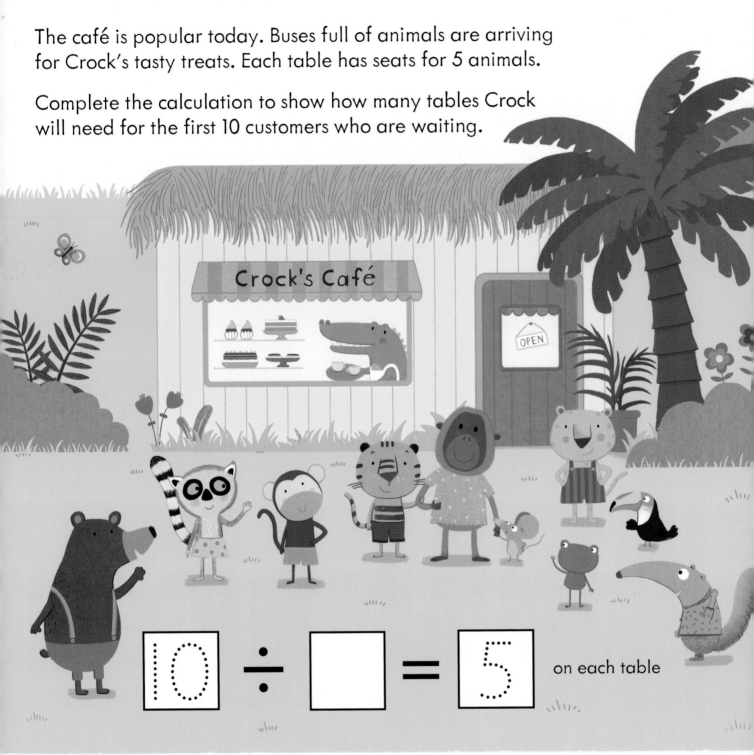

10 ÷ ☐ = 5 on each table

If you get stuck, you could turn the calculation into a multiplying one and count in 5s instead.

You could use this blank calculation to help you. Wipe it clean each time.

☐ x 5 = ☐

For every bus, complete the calculations to show how many tables will be needed.

There are 15 of us on this bus.

15

☐ ÷ ☐ = 5   on each table

There are 20 of us in here.

20

☐ ÷ ☐ = 5   on each table

There are 30 hungry animals in here.

30

☐ ÷ ☐ = 5   on each table

10 each (making equal groups of 10)

Baz and his family are waiting to go on the jungle roller-coaster. Each carriage has seats for 10 animals.

Count the bears, then complete the calculation to show how many carriages they will need.

Baz

JUNGLE-COASTER

ENTRANCE

$$\boxed{} \div \boxed{} = \boxed{10} \text{ in each carriage}$$

If you get stuck, you could turn the calculation into a multiplying one and count in 10s instead.

You could use this blank calculation to help you. Wipe it clean each time.

$$\boxed{} \times \boxed{10} = \boxed{}$$

WHOOOOSH!

Ant, Tig and Cheeky also want to go on the roller-coaster with their families. Complete the calculations to show how many carriages each family will need.

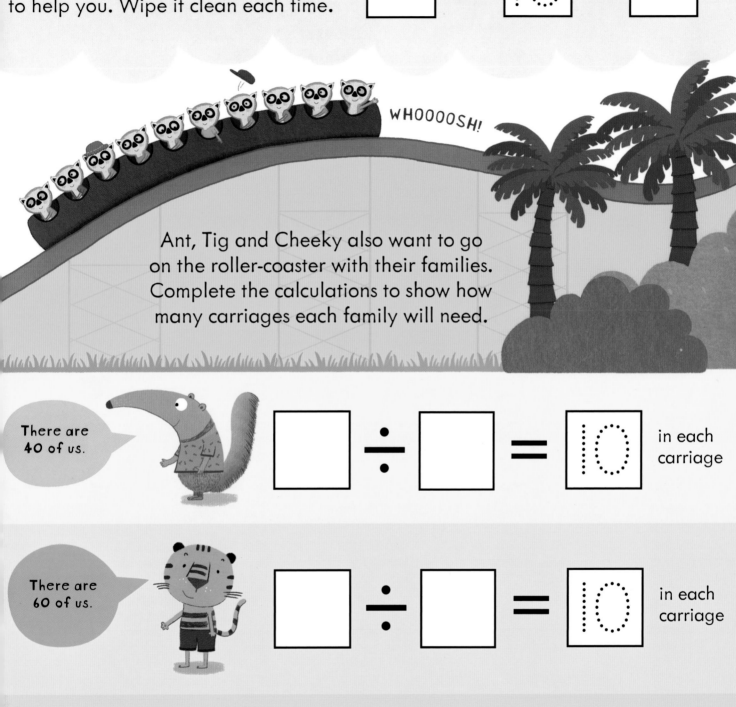

There are 40 of us.

$$\boxed{} \div \boxed{} = \boxed{10}$$ in each carriage

There are 60 of us.

$$\boxed{} \div \boxed{} = \boxed{10}$$ in each carriage

There are 80 of us.

$$\boxed{} \div \boxed{} = \boxed{10}$$ in each carriage

Dividing quiz

Find out how much you can remember about dividing by doing this quiz. Answers on page 24.

A. Tan-tan has 20 bananas. Can you remember the four different dividing calculations for 20?

Draw rings to divide up all the bananas into equal groups, then complete a calculation to show what you have done. Wipe the bananas clean after you have written a calculation.

$20 \div \boxed{} = \boxed{}$ $20 \div \boxed{} = \boxed{}$

$20 \div \boxed{} = \boxed{}$ $20 \div \boxed{} = \boxed{}$

B. Baz, Ant and Lem have written dividing calculations.
    Have they got all of their calculations right? Put a tick
    in the box next to the ones that are correct.

10 ÷ 2 = 5 ☐

20 ÷ 5 = 2 ☐

15 ÷ 3 = 5 ☐

25 ÷ 5 = 3 ☐

30 ÷ 5 = 6 ☐

8 ÷ 2 = 16 ☐

60 ÷ 6 = 10 ☐

12 ÷ 6 = 3 ☐

6 ÷ 2 = 3 ☐

C. Copy the calculations they got wrong into the blank spaces
    below, and this time write the correct answers for them.

☐ ÷ ☐ = ☐   ☐ ÷ ☐ = ☐

☐ ÷ ☐ = ☐   ☐ ÷ ☐ = ☐

D. Complete these calculations for Tig and Lep.

$40 \div 5 =$ ☐ $30 \div 2 =$ ☐ $8 \div 4 =$ ☐

$6 \div 3 =$ ☐ $80 \div 10 =$ ☐ $14 \div 2 =$ ☐

$70 \div 10 =$ ☐ $21 \div 3 =$ ☐ $35 \div 5 =$ ☐

$21 \div$ ☐ $= 3$ $24 \div$ ☐ $= 2$

$50 \div$ ☐ $= 5$ $90 \div$ ☐ $= 10$

Quiz answers

A. $20 \div 2 = 10$ $20 \div 5 = 4$ B. These are the ones the animals got right:

     $20 \div 10 = 2$ $20 \div 4 = 5$ $10 \div 2 = 5$ $60 \div 6 = 10$ $30 \div 5 = 6$

     (also $20 \div 1 = 20$ $20 \div 20 = 1$) $15 \div 3 = 5$ $6 \div 2 = 3$

C. $20 \div 5 = 4$ D. $40 \div 5 = 8$ $30 \div 2 = 15$ $8 \div 4 = 2$

     $25 \div 5 = 5$ $6 \div 3 = 2$ $80 \div 10 = 8$ $14 \div 2 = 7$

     $8 \div 2 = 4$ $70 \div 10 = 7$ $21 \div 3 = 7$ $35 \div 5 = 7$

     $12 \div 6 = 2$ $21 \div 7 = 3$ $24 \div 12 = 2$

                 $50 \div 10 = 5$ $90 \div 9 = 10$

Score 1 point for each correct answer and write your score in this box:
If you want to get a higher score, wipe the pages clean and try again.

☐ 26